Michael Rosen was brought up in London. He originally tried to study medicine before starting to write poems and stories. His poems are about all kinds of things – but always important things – from toothpaste to chewing bus tickets!

*Some other books by Michael Rosen*

*Poetry*

CENTRALLY HEATED KNICKERS

LUNCH BOXES DON'T FLY

MICHAEL ROSEN'S BOOK OF VERY SILLY
POEMS *(with Shoo Rayner)*

QUICK, LET'S GET OUT OF HERE
*(with Quentin Blake)*

YOU TELL ME *(with Roger McGough)*

YOU WAIT TILL I'M OLDER THAN YOU!
*(with Shoo Rayner)*

*Picture Books*

YOU CAN'T CATCH ME *(with Quentin Blake)*

MOVING *(with Sophy Williams)*

MINI BEASTIES *(with Alan Baker)*

*Some other books by Korky Paul*

AESOP'S FUNKY FABLES *(with Vivian French)*

THE RASCALLY CAKE *(with Jeanne Willis)*
Winner of the Children's Book Award

# Michael Rosen

# Uncle Billy
# Being Silly

*Illustrated by Korky Paul*

PUFFIN BOOKS

PUFFIN BOOKS

Published by the Penguin Group
Penguin Books Ltd, 27 Wrights Lane, London W8 5TZ, England
Penguin Putnam Inc., 375 Hudson Street, New York, New York 10014, USA
Penguin Books Australia Ltd, Ringwood, Victoria, Australia
Penguin Books Canada Ltd, 10 Alcorn Avenue, Toronto, Ontario, Canada M4V 3B2
Penguin Books India (P) Ltd, 11 Community Centre, Panchsheel Park,
New Delhi – 110 017, India
Penguin Books (NZ) Ltd, Cnr Rosedale and Airborne Roads, Albany,
Auckland, New Zealand
Penguin Books (South Africa) (Pty) Ltd, 5 Watkins Street, Denver Ext 4,
Johannesburg 2094, South Africa

On the World Wide Web at: www.penguin.com

Penguin Books Ltd, Registered Offices: Harmondsworth, Middlesex, England

First published 2001
3 5 7 9 10 8 6 4 2

'Eddie and the Shreddies' reprinted from *Quick, Let's Get Out of Here*
(André Deutsch Ltd, 1983) copyright © Michael Rosen 1983

Printed in Hong Kong by Midas Printing Ltd

British Library Cataloguing in Publication Data
A CIP catalogue record for this book is available from the British Library

ISBN 0–141–30021–3

*For my ever-growing family – M.R.*

*To Bianca Moxley – K.P.*

# ··· Contents ···

# Going Through the Old Photos

Who's that?
That's your Auntie Mabel
and that's me
under the table.

Who's that?
That's Uncle Billy.
Who's that?
Me being silly.

Who's that
licking a lolly?
I'm not sure
but I think it's Polly.

Who's that
behind the tree?
I don't know,
I can't see.
Could be you.
Could be me.

Who's that?
Baby Joe.
Who's that?
I don't know.

Who's that standing
on his head?
Turn it round.
It's Uncle Ted.

3

# Eddie and the Shreddies

The other day Eddie
was eating his Shreddies –
you know what Shreddies are:
those little bits of cardboard
you have for breakfast.

Sometimes he forgets where his
 mouth is
and he stuffs a Shreddie in his ear.
Doesn't worry him
He takes it out and puts it in his
 mouth.

Anyway,
I left my hairbrush on the table
while he was eating his Shreddies
and I went out of the room.

While I was out
Eddie found somewhere else
to put his Shreddies.
On my hairbrush.

When I came back in
I picked up my hairbrush
and brushed my hair ...

Yuk.

Shreddies in my hair.
I looked at Eddie,
Eddie's looking at me.
Big grin on his face.

I knew he had done it.
Last week he put pepper in the
    raisins.

# My Mum's Mum and My Dad's Dad

My mum's mum and my dad's dad
met my mum's dad and my dad's
  mum
my mum's daughter and my dad's
  son
met my dad and met my mum.

9

# Mum Reads to Me
# Every Night

Mum reads to me every night

she's reading *The Tailor of
  Gloucester*

she sits on the edge of the bed
and reads in a sing-song voice
that drifts on for ever

I tell her
her voice is sleepy
and she gets all huffy
and says:
well, I shan't bother then
what a thing to say
really
I don't think I'll bother.

'Sleepy'
was how I liked it
I wasn't complaining.

# Dad's a Climbing Frame

Dad's a climbing frame
we're climbing on Dad
we've got a climbing frame
let's go mad.

# I'm in My Mum

I'm in my mum

on one hand
one thumb
on the other hand
another one

I'm in my mum

in the middle of me
I've got
tcha-boom sha
tcha-boom sha
tcha-boom sha
a heart
in the middle of me
I hear
ca-boom
ca-boom
ca-boom
her heart

in here

we go

tcha-boom sha

tcha-boom sha

tcha-boom sha

ca-boom

tcha-boom sha

tcha-boom sha

tcha-boom sha

ca-boom

I'm in my mum.

# My Brother's on the Floor Roaring

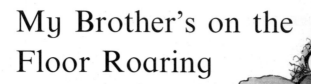

My brother's on the floor roaring
my brother's on the floor roaring
why is my brother on the floor
    roaring?
My brother is on the floor roaring
because he's supposed to finish his
    beans
before he has his pudding

16

he says he wants his pudding
NOW

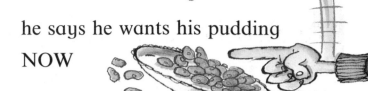

but they won't let him
so now my brother is ... on the floor
   roaring.

They're saying:
I give you one more chance to finish
   those beans
or you don't go to Tony's,
but he's not listening because ...
he's on the floor roaring.

He's getting told off
I'm not
I've eaten my beans.

Do you know what I'm doing now?
I'm eating my pudding
and ... he's on the floor roaring.
If he wasn't ... on the floor roaring
he'd see me eating my pudding
and if he looked really close
he might see a little tiny smile
just at the corner of my mouth.
But he's not looking ...
he's on the floor roaring.

The pudding is OK

it's not wonderful

not wonderful enough

to be sitting on the floor and

   roaring about

unless you're my brother.

# Family

At school today
We had to say who's in our family.
I said: my dad, my sister and
Tigger.
The boy in front said:
So where's your mum then?
I said: Where's your brains then?

He said: Who's Tigger?

I said: Tigger's our cat.

He said: Well Tigger doesn't count then.

I said: Of course Tigger doesn't count, he's a cat.

He said: I meant he's not in your family.

I said: I don't care what you meant.

# Invitation

When you're very nearly four
sometimes things look completely
terrible
even when they're not.

My younger brother
was going to have a party.
He did an invitation card on the
computer
with Mum.
It said: Come to my party.
It's going to be really great.

He told Mum who he wanted to
come.

They wrote the people's names on
the envelopes.

'There!' said Mum,
'we did it.'

Then he burst into tears.

'What's the matter?' she said.

He wouldn't say.

He just cried and cried and cried.

It went on for hours.

But he wouldn't say.

In the end Mum said,
'You talk to him. You might get it
  out of him.'

So I asked him what it was all
about
and he said, 'I can't go to my
party.'
I said, 'Why not?'
And he said, 'Because I haven't been
invited.'

When you're very nearly four
sometimes things look completely
terrible
even when they're not.

# Shmutter

OK, so laugh!

OK, so I thought it was an English
word.

How should I know it isn't English?

My mum and dad call it a shmutter,

my brother calls it a shmutter,

so I call it a shmutter.

OK, so laugh!

OK, so I thought it was the English
word.

Yeah, sure I heard some people call
it a tea towel

Yeah, yeah, I know some people call
it a drying-up cloth.

But we call it a shmutter, OK?

That's what we all call it in my
house.

A shmutter.

Just like that.

Yeah, yeah, very funny.

I'm telling you, I thought it was the English word, OK?

OK, so laugh.

Go on.

Just laugh.

Laugh, laugh, laugh.

Shmutter, shmutter, shmutter.

# At the Zoo

When we see the lions and tigers
and there's the sign These Animals
are Dangerous,
My dad says, 'They're like
kangaroos.
See the sign? These animals are
dangaroos.'

# Da –

Once my brother was in trouble
big big trouble
and he was sent to his room
and I went upstairs to talk to him
and he told me how it was really
really unfair
and it was all Dad's fault
and didn't I agree it was Dad's
fault?

And I felt sorry for my brother
and I wondered how I could help
and suddenly I thought, I know,
I could shout something really
horrible
about our dad
and that would make my brother
feel better
because then my brother would
know that I was on his side.

So I thought,

What shall I shout?

I know,

I'll shout,

'Stinky old Dad!'

I'll shout it really really loud

and that'll help,

that'll make my brother feel better.

So I stood up on my bed
and I started to shout,
'Stinky old Dad!'
But the thing is,
I only got as far as,
'STINKY OLD DA —'
when he walked in.

He didn't hear.
He just walked straight in
and had another go at my brother.
And all the time he was going on
and on
we were trying not to laugh

but when he walked out
we fell in a great heap of giggles,
saying, 'Stinky old Da –, stinky old
Da –!'
over and over again.

# Arrows

Me and my friend Harrybo
we were playing arrows.
You take the grass
that's got pointed tops.
They fly through the air
and you can throw them at things.
We found this open window
on the wall of the alley
by my house.

We were aiming the arrows
at the open window.
Mostly they missed.
Every now and then
one went in.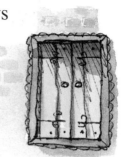
'Yeahhhhhhhhh!' we shouted.
'Arrow! Fifty points.'
We were a good few feet
away from the window
so it wasn't easy.

Then all of a sudden
this man appeared in the alley.
It was Baldy, the old bald bloke
in charge of the builders' yard
down there.
He came marching up to us
and stood there in front of us
in his overalls.
You could see he was furious.
He held out his fist.
I thought he was going to punch
one of us.

His fist, though,
was kind of the wrong way up,
palm upwards.

He looked down at it.
'What do you think this is, eh?'
he shouts.
We looked down too.
There stuck between his fingers
in the fist
was ...

... an arrow.

He must have been sitting at his
desk
inside the office
with his fist on the table
and one of the arrows must have
flown
through the window
and landed right in it.

'Eh? Well?' he shouts.

'We were playing arrows,' says
   Harrybo.

'Clear off and play it somewhere
   else,'

he says.

We scarpered.

Then,

when we sat down round at

Harrybo's place

we talked about how the arrow

must have gone flying through the

window

and landed on him

and we imagined Baldy sitting there

and the arrow coming from nowhere

wheeeeeeeeeeeeee

and just happening to land on his

fist

wow, what a shot!

and we laughed and laughed.

Then,
much later,
Harrybo said,
'I wonder whose arrow it was ...
... mine or yours ...'

And neither of us knew
and neither of us ever will know.

# Indian Restaurant

We all went out to an Indian
restaurant
and we spent hours and hours
choosing what we wanted.
'What's poppadom?'
'Poppadoms are big crisp things.'
'What's korma?'
'Korma's kind of creamy ...'
'What's aloo?'
'Aloo is potato.'
'What's sag?'
'Sag is spinach.'

'What's channa?'
'Channa is chick pea.'
'What's very hot?'
'Vindaloo.'
'What's mild?'
'Try chicken tikka.'

We went on and on and on
making sure we knew
what everything was
and in the end
we chose some things.

Then,

as we were waiting

two men came in

and sat down at the table

next to us.

The waiter went over.

'Hi, Abdul,' says one of them,

'fish and chips twice,' he says,

'cheers!'


And we all looked at each other

not daring to even smile.

# Flats

Our flat's over an old shop.
Chris's flat's in a new block.
Our flat's got dark stairs.
Chris's flat's got a silver lift.

Our flat's got a cracked backyard.
Chris's flat's got a marked-up
playground.
Our flat's door opens into the yard.
Chris's flat's door opens on to a
balcony.

Chris's bedroom walls are smooth.

My bedroom walls are lumpy.

Our flat looks down into the street.

Chris's flat looks out over London.

I'd like to live in Chris's flat.

# At the Pictures

Scary movie
Wooo wooo
Sitting in the dark
Wooo wooo
Great big teeth
Wooo wooo
Bulging veins
Wooo wooo
Crashing noise
Wooo wooo
Getting nearer
Wooo wooo
Staring eyes
Wooo wooo
Really huge

Wooo wooo
Feeling small
Wooo wooo
Hands sweaty
Wooo wooo
Dad next to me
Wooo wooo
In his old coat
Wooo wooo
Grab his arm
Wooo wooo
Hide under the coat
Wooo wooo
Scary movie
Wooo wooo
Not so scary
Phewwwwwwwwwwwww!

# Coming Home

Flying home from holiday
Flying home from holiday
All of us together
All of us together

Landing at the airport
Landing at the airport
All of us together
All of us together

In the airport bus
All of us together
All of us together

In the big hall
All of us together
All of us together

Then mum goes one way
Dad goes another way
Mum's got one passport
Dad's got another

We're with Mum
Dad's on his own
We go through
So where's Dad now?

Waiting for Dad
Waiting for Dad
Mum's biting her lips
Waiting for Dad

Waiting for Dad
Waiting for Dad
Mum holding our hands
Waiting for Dad

Waiting for Dad
Waiting for Dad
Waiting for Dad
Then it's:

There he is!
There he is!
He's got through
He's got through

So it's
All of us together
All of us together
All of us together
Heading home
All of us together
Heading home.